Specimen Sight-Reading Tests for Baritone, Euphonium and Tuba 𝄢

Grades 1–5

ABRSM

1
Allegretto
p
f
p

2
Moderato
p
f
p
f
p

3
Andante
p
f
p

Allegro
4
p
f
p
Allegro
5
f
p
f
p
Andante
6
p
f
p
Alla marcia
7
f
p
f

Andante
8
p
f
p
f
Moderato
9
f
p
f
p

Allegro
10
f
p
f

Allegro
11
f
p
f

Allegro
12
p
mf
p
mf
p
Andante
13
p
f
p
Alla marcia
14
f
p
f
Moderato
15
mf
f
mf
p

Moderato
1
mp
f
mp
f
mp
Alla marcia
2
f
p
f
Moderato
3
mf
f
p
Moderato
4
f
p
f

Allegro
5
p
f
p
f
p
f
Andante
6
p
mf
p
Moderato
7
p
f
p
f
Moderato
8
f
p
f

Allegro
9
p
mf
f
p

Ritmico
10
f
p
f

Allegro
11
f
p
cresc.
f
p

Andante
12
p
f
p

Moderato
1
mf
p
f
p
Sostenuto
2
mp
mf
p
March
3
f
p
f
p
f
Allegro
4
mf
f
p
f

Moderato
5
p
f
p
f
p
Risoluto
6
mf
f
p
Allegro
7
f
p
f

Moderato
8
p
f
p
mf

Risoluto
9
f
p
f
p
Moderato
10
p
f
p
Moderato
11
mf
p
f
p

Giocoso
12
p
f
p
f

Risoluto
1
f
p
f
Allegro
2
p
f
p
f
Largo
3
p
f
p
f
p
mf
mf
p
Moderato
4
f
p
f
p
f
p
f

Sostenuto
5
Moderato
6
Andante
7
Allegro
8

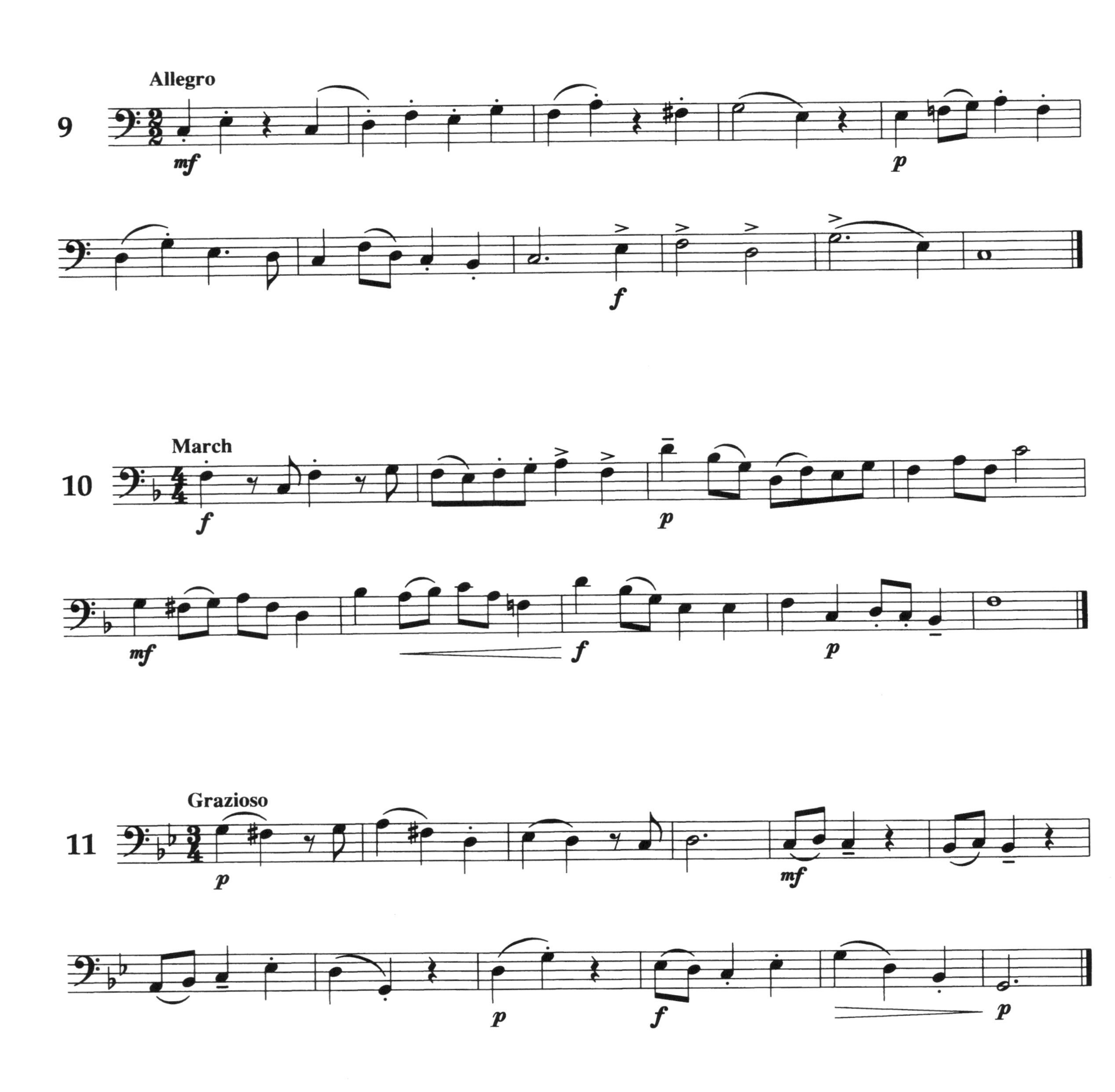
Allegro
9
mf
p
f
March
10
f
p
mf
f
p
Grazioso
11
p
mf
p
f
p

Scherzando
12
f
p
mf
f

Marziale
1
f
p
f
p

Ritmico
2
mf
p
f

Grazioso
3
p
f

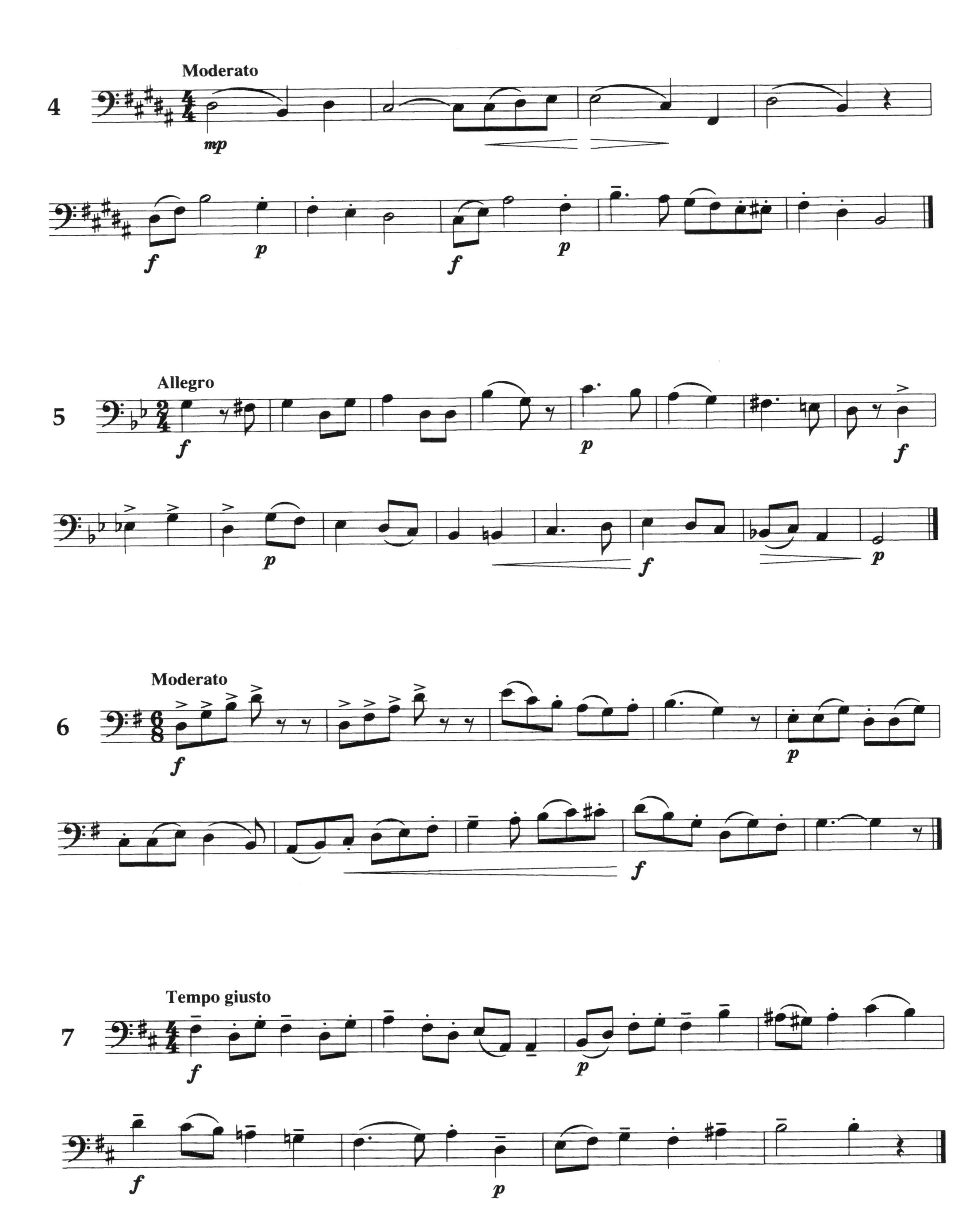

4
Moderato
mp
f
p
f
p
5
Allegro
f
p
f
p
f
p
6
Moderato
f
p
f
7
Tempo giusto
f
p
f
p

Moderato
8
f
p
f
p
f
Scherzando
9
f
p
f
p
mf
f
Alla marcia
10
f
p
f
Cantabile
11
p
cresc.
f
p

E♭ Tuba

Sostenuto
1
p
mf
p

Alla marcia
2
f
p
f

Andante
3
p
f
p

Andante
4
p
f
p
f

Moderato
5
p
f
p
f
p

B♭ Tuba

Andante
1
p
mf
f
p
Allegro
2
p
mf
p
mf
p
Moderato
3
mf
f
mf
p

C Tuba

F Tuba

E♭ Tuba

Moderato
1
f
p
f
p
f
Ritmico
2
f
p
f
Alla marcia
3
f
p
f
Moderato
4
mf
f
p

Moderato

5

p

cresc.

B♭ Tuba

C Tuba

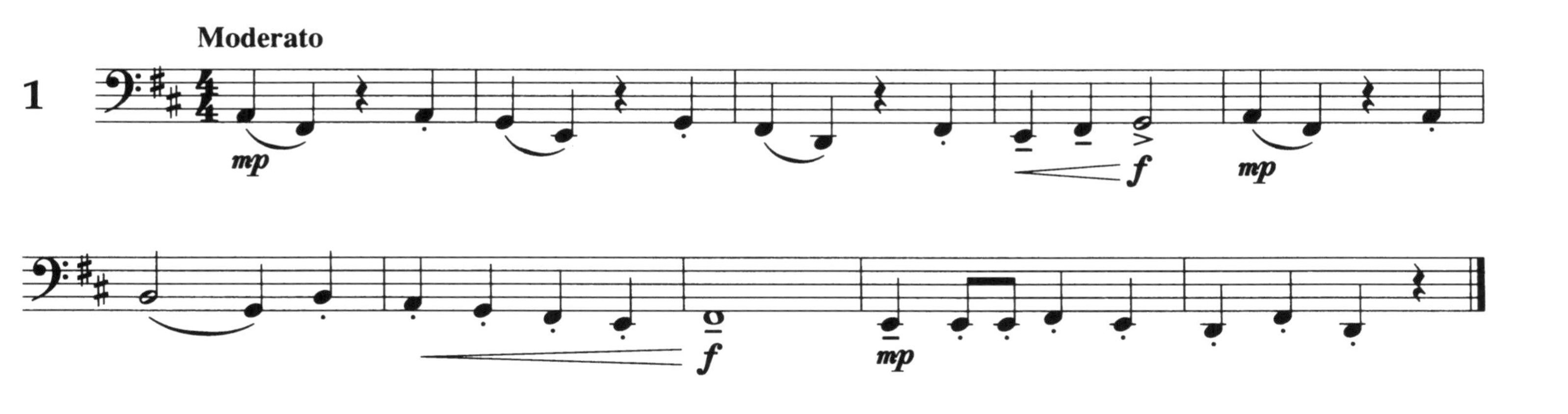

F Tuba

E♭ Tuba

AB 2486

Risoluto
5
mf
f
p

B♭ Tuba

Allegro
1
mf
f
p
f
Moderato
2
p
f
p
Andante
3
p
mf
f
p
f

C Tuba

Allegretto
1
mf
p
f
Andante
2
p
f
p

F Tuba

Allegro
1
f
p
f
p
Moderato
2
mf
p
f
p

E♭ Tuba

Allegro
1
f
p
f
p
Allegro
2
p
f
p
f
Grazioso
3
p
mf
p
f
p
Moderato
4
p
mf
p
cresc.
f
p

B♭ Tuba

C Tuba

E♭ Tuba

Moderato
1
mp
f
p
f
p
Moderato
2
mf
p
cresc.
f
p
Vivo
3
p
cresc.
f
Moderato
4
f
p
mf
p
f
p
f

B♭ Tuba

C Tuba

F Tuba

Printed and bound in Great Britain by
Caligraving Limited Thetford Norfolk

Typeset by Musonix